Al K...
And Tl...

Written by

Illustrated by Kerry Gemmill

Contents   Page

Nelson
an International Thomson Publishing company ITP®

Al Kalifa
And The Nile

With these characters ...

Al Kalifa

The Pharaoh
And Queen

"King Ahmose had

Setting the scene ...

Deep within the magnificent, mysterious palace
of the Pharaoh, Al Kalifa learns that he has been
chosen to carry out a plan that will change the
mighty Nile River forever. He is at once scared
and honoured. He knows that if he succeeds, his
name will be remembered for thousands of years.
But if he fails, a terrible fate will await him. He
gathers his plans and his workers and starts to
build a huge dam. But the river is not so easily
tamed ...

ordered the dam to be built;
and so it would be."

Chapter 1.

Inside a dark tomb, near the Great Pyramid, a stone wall is covered in ancient Egyptian writing and pictures. It tells the story of a man who lived three thousand years ago, and who was buried in the tomb:

"Here lies Al Kalifa, builder of a massive stone dam. His wish was to be known as a great man who changed the Nile River. Sadly, that is not the way he is remembered. His story is told through the writing and pictures on the walls surrounding his tomb. Read his story and learn from his mistakes."

Al Kalifa waited anxiously outside the royal palace, feeling a mixture of fear and excitement. He had been summoned to the palace of the Pharaoh, King Ahmose. King Ahmose ruled over all the lands around the great River Nile in Egypt. He was a rich and powerful man and, if summoned, you were either about to be included in an important event—or punished for breaking the King's law. Al Kalifa stood outside, his mouth dry from the dust and sand of the desert.

Al Kalifa had travelled for three days, through the hot, dry desert to reach the palace. His feet and legs were tired. His skin was burnt by the sun. During the whole journey, he had tried to imagine why King Ahmose wanted to talk to him. He was soon to find out.

Just then, a royal soldier interrupted his thoughts by heaving open the forbidding doors to the palace. He was dressed in a shimmering white cloth, with a magnificent, golden head-dress. He carried a long, heavy spear made of black wood, with a sharp point.

"Come with me," he said sternly. Al Kalifa looked at the soldier's face to see if he could guess what was about to happen. The soldier stared at him with no expression.

As Al Kalifa followed the soldier into the great palace, his legs felt weak. He tried desperately to control his fear. If he trembled when he met the Pharaoh, it would be extremely embarrassing. The guard led him through a long, stone corridor, decorated with intricate paintings and ornate statues of the King's family. On the ceiling were paintings of the Egyptian gods that everyone feared.

Everyone believed that the Pharaohs had been especially chosen by their gods to rule Egypt. He felt even more scared. He tried to walk calmly and to breathe normally. But being in the Pharaoh's palace made Al Kalifa feel as small as a beetle.

The soldier reached a huge golden door, three times as high as a person. It was carved with beautiful pictures, symbols and writing. The soldier raised his spear and banged three times on the door. Slowly the door opened, and Al Kalifa looked in awe at the sight before him.

Chapter 2.

He entered a huge room which was more beautiful than any he had ever dreamed of. Magnificent statues stood all around, watching him. Rich, deep red curtains hung from every wall. There was so much gold and so many precious jewels on all the walls and furniture that Al Kalifa wanted to reach out and touch everything. But he did not dare. A group of figures stood around a raised platform. Some wore masks, so he could not tell whether they were humans, statues or even animals. All stood silently, looking at Al Kalifa.

But Al Kalifa felt the most terror when he looked closely at the platform. A beam of light shone through a long, narrow window in the roof, down onto the platform. And, in the middle of the platform, were two golden thrones decorated with carved wings.

On one throne sat a beautiful woman, the
queen. Her skin was golden brown and her royal
clothes shone like the moon. Beside her, on the
other throne, sat the most powerful man he had
ever met: King Ahmose, the mighty Pharaoh, ruler
of all Egypt.

Al Kalifa fell to his knees and bowed his head. King Ahmose waved the soldier away and looked at Al Kalifa without smiling. Al Kalifa feared the worst. What was going to happen to him?

Then one of the fearsome masked figures moved over to him, and touched him on the shoulder. Without speaking, he beckoned to Al Kalifa to stand up. Even though his legs were shaking, Al Kalifa obeyed.

The Pharaoh spoke, in a slow, deep voice.

"Al Kalifa, builder of the magnificent Memphis
pyramid, do not be afraid. We have chosen you
for a very important task. If you succeed, your
name will be remembered forever."

Al Kalifa nodded. He did not dare to ask
what would happen if he failed.

The Pharaoh asked one of the masked figures to hand him a roll of papyrus. When the papyrus was unrolled, Al Kalifa could see that it was a map of Egypt and the Nile River.

"Our land is mostly dry, harsh desert," explained the King. "In the desert, there is no food or water, only rolling hills of sand and scorching heat."

"We can't grow food in the desert, but we can grow our crops along the Nile River," continued King Ahmose. "Each year, there are heavy rains and the river floods. With the floods, come good soil and water. When the floods go down, we plant crops in the fertile mud left behind."

"For the past two years, we have not had good floods," said Ahmose. "It has made life hard for our people, because we cannot grow enough food."

The King folded his arms and looked directly into Al Kalifa's eyes.

"We have decided to control the Nile. We want you to build a stone dam across it."

Al Kalifa was astonished. Immediately he
understood that, with a dam across the Nile, the
Egyptians could control when and how much of
their land was flooded with the life-giving water
and soil. But the dam would be an enormous
risk. No-one had tried to change the Nile before.

Even so, he could see that Ahmose was
determined. This was his chance to please his
Pharaoh and to become famous. Al Kalifa took a
deep breath.

"I will be honoured to build your dam,
Pharaoh," he said, trying to look confident.

Chapter 3.

For weeks, Al Kalifa explored the Nile and the surrounding lands. He walked, sailed and studied the river in many places. It was difficult to find the perfect position to build the dam. Some sites were too close to villages. Some sites were sacred places, with temples on them. Some were too wide, rocky or deep. Finally, he decided on the best place to build Egypt's first dam.

One day, when the sun seemed even hotter than usual, he showed the site to his team of dam builders. He brought out his plans, drawn up on a long scroll of papyrus.

"Study this site and these plans carefully. We cannot make any mistakes. We must not fail!"

He pointed at the other side of the river. "We will build a low stone wall across the Nile, while it is at its lowest level."

"Our low wall will trap the water behind it.
When we have finished building it, we will build
upwards quickly so, as the water rises, it does not
spill over. In the middle, we will build massive
wooden gates. With the gates, we can let water
out from behind the dam whenever we need it."

Al Kalifa looked at his workers.

"For the first time in history, our people will not have to worry about hunger. We will have plenty of water for our crops, stored up behind the gates of our dam."

The workers looked worried. They were good at building pyramids, not dams. It sounded dangerous, but they had no choice. King Ahmose had ordered the dam to be built; and so it would be.

From a quarry nearby, hundreds of stone cutters carved huge blocks of stone. Hundreds of other workers were given the job of pulling the huge blocks into the correct places. Month after month, Al Kalifa watched as a thin line of stone was gradually laid across the Nile.

The work was hard, and everyone was exhausted by the time the hot sun disappeared each night.

But at dawn, the hundreds of workers started all over again, cutting, dragging and placing massive blocks of stone across the river. And each day, the scorching sun beat down on everyone. The sands from the desert blew into hundreds of mouths, eyes and nostrils.

As the workers heaved the gigantic blocks into place, the dam grew higher and higher. Wooden gates, as large as houses, were set into the wall. Al Kalifa ordered that a small gap be left in the middle, for the Nile to keep flowing through while they were building. After almost a year of work, the gap was ready to be filled. The line of stones stood as high as three men.

Al Kalifa sent a message to the Pharaoh, explaining that the first part of the dam was almost complete. A week later, he received a reply. The Pharaoh would come in person to watch the final stones being put in place.

The news spread quickly through the workers.
"The Pharaoh himself will come," they
whispered to each other. The most powerful man
in the land would see what a fantastic job they
had done! He would no doubt be pleased with
their work.

Chapter 4.

On the day of the Pharaoh's visit, the sun shone even hotter. The workers waited anxiously at the centre of the dam, ready to lower the final stones into place. Finally, a great procession that no-one would ever forget appeared in the distance.

A hundred soldiers, dressed in their finest uniforms, marched towards them. Twenty drummers beat out a slow, deep rhythm as everyone marched closer. Masked figures, dressed in gold and brightly coloured robes, walked behind. And huge men carried an enormous golden platform on their shoulders. Shining in the sunlight, sitting proudly on the platform, were the Pharaoh and his beautiful queen.

At the edge of the river, the platform carrying the Pharaoh and the queen was gently lowered to the ground. The Pharaoh stood up and looked at Al Kalifa, standing on top of the dam with his workers.

"You and your workers have done well,
Al Kalifa," he called out loudly. "Your work will
prove that Egyptians are clever dam builders, as
well as pyramid builders."

King Ahmose raised his arm.

"Finish the dam!" he commanded.

At that moment, everyone heard a low deep, rumble. They looked towards the south, where the noise had come from. The sky had darkened. Tall, dark clouds looked threatening as they moved swiftly towards them. Al Kalifa's heart beat faster.

Al Kalifa turned his back on the approaching thunderstorm and shouted at the workers to lower the final stones. Ropes creaked and men grunted as the heavy blocks were lifted and fitted into place. Raindrops as large as pebbles splattered noisily all around them. Then, everyone heard another low, deep rumbling sound. But this time, it was *not* thunder.

Chapter 5.

Al Kalifa turned around in alarm. Down the river, in the distance, he saw what was making the sound. A huge wall of water was rushing down the Nile from the south. It was a furious flash flood. And it was heading straight for them! The raging thunderstorm far in the south had dumped an enormous amount of water into the Nile. Within seconds, the water would pound against their new dam. It might be destroyed!

"Raise the stones!" he screamed. His only hope was to let some water flow through the gap. But it was too late. The stones were already lowered. Although hundreds of workers pulled with all their might, they could not raise them again. The flash flood hurtled towards them with a frightening roar.

Suddenly, the water slammed into the dam. Huge waves crashed off the stone wall, and surged all around. With nowhere to go, except sideways, the water swept along the wall. Washing away everything in its path, the water cut a deep channel across the flat land to the east. And still the water kept surging against the dam.

Al Kalifa clung desperately to one of the ropes attached to a huge stone, as the water rushed past him at a ferocious speed. Many of his workers were not so lucky. They were swept away, yelling and screaming, by the angry river.

From the west side of the dam, the Pharaoh and his group watched in horror. This was the worst disaster they had seen.

Lightning cracked across the sky. Heavy rain beat down on the rising river and the surrounding land. Al Kalifa watched helplessly as their year's work was rapidly destroyed and his workers were lost.

But although the flash flood had been a disaster, worse was yet to come. After a week, the flood waters lowered, and the Egyptians saw that a truly terrible thing had happened.

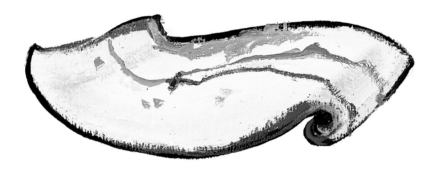

Rather than returning to its normal course, the Nile had changed direction. Instead of flowing through the fertile lands to the north, the dam had caused it to flow through the desert, away from the farmlands where people lived and planted crops.

Chapter 6.

After seven years of hunger, the river finally returned to its original course. But life for the Egyptians took much longer to improve. The famine had caused much sickness, as people had been forced to eat unhealthy food and to drink unclean water. Even King Ahmose had become very ill, from a terrible disease called cholera.

Within weeks, Egypt's new Pharaoh decided that the people of Egypt would never again try to change their natural environment. They had learned their lesson in a most disastrous way.

And poor Al Kalifa? He spent the rest of his life helping people rebuild their homes and their towns.

The new Pharaoh never invited him back to the palace. Instead of being known as the man who changed the Nile, his name was only ever mentioned as a warning.

"You must always treat the world around you with respect. Sometimes, if we try to change our environment, there can be terrible consequences. Remember the mistakes of Al Kalifa and King Ahmose," people said for years to come.

And so it was. In a thousand years time, people would look upon the bare sands and scorching heat of the desert, where all that remained of Al Kalifa and King Ahmose were ancient stone tombs.

"Here, in the tomb of Al Kalifa, you have read his story on the walls that surround you. Learn from his mistakes. If you wish to change your world, beware! It may change in a way you do not expect!"

"Mighty, the Nile ..."

Mighty, the Nile carries life to the desert
Mighty, the Nile carries the dust of the years
Mighty, the Nile carries away the old and leaves the new
Mighty, the Nile carries memories
Of Pharaohs
Who once thought
They were mighty, too.

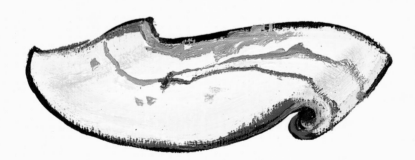